1

bad   cat   fat   glad

Never let your pussy – – –
Eat sweets, for that would make hi[m]
And it would make his teeth go – –
I think the mice would be quite – – – –.

2

fat   hat   sat   that

The lady wore a great big – – –,
It was like a bird, now fancy – – – –,
And on the top a big bee – – –,
It's just as well that she was – – –.

3 How many words can you find that rhyme
with "**sad**"?

1

bed   hen   Ted   ten

Every night Ned went to – – –,
With this cuddly little – – –,
His dogs, his cats, his little red – – –,
Altogether his bed held – – –.

2

again   leg   Len   Meg

"I'll never play with you – – – – –,"
That's what he said, my best friend – – –,
I did not mean to kick his – – –,
I meant to kick his sister, – – –.

3

Find as many words as you can that rhyme with
"**men**".

1

bit   it   sill   thrill

Sanjeet thought it was a – – – – – –,
Sitting on the window – – – –,
It's six floors up, that's quite a – – –,
If he falls down that will be – –.

2

bit   kit   fit   quit

The boy scout packed up all his – – –,
And said, "I'll walk a little – – –,"
He walked a mile and then he – – – –,
He surely can't be very – – –.

3

Try to find as many words as you can to rhyme with "**sit**".

1   **hot   pot   odd   trod**

The animal looked very – – –,
As down the jungle path he – – – –,
In one large hand, he held a – – –,
Of pea soup, which was very – – –.

2   **clot   dog   frog   not**

The odd boy went out with a – – – –,
On a lead, just like a – – –,
He really is a silly – – – –,
Dogs like walking, frogs do – – –.

3   How many words can you find with the
same ending as "**cot**"?

4

1

bug   dug   tum   yum-yum

While in the garden Jimmy – – –,
He found a most enormous – – –,
He ate the thing, and rubbed his – – –,
And said, "I liked that bug, – – –-– – –."

2

fluff   fun   puff   bun

One day a little bit of – – – – –,
Escaped from Mother's powder – – – –,
It had a little bit of – – –,
Then landed on a sugar – – –.

3

Can you find some words that rhyme with
"**sum**" and have the same ending?

5

1

cage   mane   plain   rage

I went to stroke the lion's – – – –,
He did not like it, that was – – – – –,
He roared at me in such a – – – –,
I'm glad that he was in a – – – –.

2

brake   drake   lake   shake

The motorist forgot to – – – – –,
His car went splashing in the – – – –,
With rage the man began to – – – – –,
While on his head, sat a big fat – – – – –.

3 Write down as many words as you can that rhyme with "**make**".

1　　bite　　fine　　fright　　mine

I once got an awful – – – – – –,
When the dog gave me a – – – –,
If that's the way he wants it— – – – –,
I'll bite his leg if he bites – – – –.

2　　fire　　hide　　inside　　wire

Bobby set the house on – – – –,
Playing with electric – – – –,
Now he's run away to – – – –,
Because a policeman's gone – – – – – –.

3　How many words can you find that rhyme
with "**line**"?

1

arose   **joke**   **nose**   **poke**

One day Terry, for a – – – –,
Gave a crocodile a – – – –,
The crocodile at once – – – – –,
And bit right off poor Terry's – – – –.

2

before   **bore**   **more**   **roar**

A dinosaur once gave a – – – –,
He doesn't do it any – – – –,
He's now extinct, not like – – – – – –,
To be extinct must be a – – – –.

3

Find as many words as you can that
rhyme with "**tore**".

1

blue   clue   true   you

I wonder why the sky is – – – –,
I'm sure I haven't got a – – – –,
I only know that it is – – – –,
I can't explain it though—can – – –?

2

brute   cute   flute   jute

The wizard was a horrid – – – – –,
He wore a tunic made of – – – –,
His pet, the dragon looked quite – – – –,
He wore a hat and played the – – – – –.

3

See how many words you can find that
rhyme with "**June**".

1   **brown   crown   howl   owl**

The hat she wore was coloured – – – – –,
It had some feathers on the – – – – –,
The boys and girls began to – – – –,
She looked just like a tawny – – –.

2   **bow   flower   Meiow   power**

The fairy used her magic – – – – –,
To turn the cat into a – – – – – –,
And then the fairy gave a – – –,
The dandelion, it said, ''– – – – –.''

3 How many words can you find that rhyme
with ''**cow**''?

1

arrow   marrow   sorrow   tomorrow

Silly Billy shot an – – – – –,
Through his father's favourite – – – – – –,
Billy then was filled with – – – – – –,
Father's coming home – – – – – – – –.

2

growing   grows   showing   snows

In the summer when things are – – – – – – –,
Blossoms and flowers are gaily – – – – – – –,
But in the winter, when it – – – – –,
Only the little snowdrop – – – – –.

3

Can you find some words that rhyme with "**blow**"?

1

sawing   saw   drawing
see-saw   sawn   lawn

I took my dad's old rusty – – –,
And quickly started – – – – – –,
I meant to make a fine – – –-- – –,
I should have made a – – – – – – –.
It would have stood upon the – – – –,
But it was squint when it was – – – –.

2

children   crawl   paw   saw

"Stop!" bawled the – – – – – – – –,
When they – – –
The blind mouse – – – – –
Up the sleeping cat's – – –.

3

Make a list of the words you can think of
ending with "**aw**".

1

boat   float   groan   loan

Billy asked me for a – – – –,
Of my little – – – –,
He broke the mast, I gave a – – – – –,
For now it will not – – – – –.

2

groan   moan   road   toad

Once a silly little – – – –,
Was playing on a busy – – – –,
A car hit him and made him – – – –,
And turned his croak into a – – – – –.

3

How many words can you find that rhyme
with "**coat**"?

1

pea   sea   tea   tree

When I was fishing in the – – –,
I caught a box, a bit of – – – –,
A bicycle, a small green – – –,
I think I'll have the pea for – – –.

2

beak   hear   near   speak

The robin had a magic – – – –,
And do you know that it could – – – – –?
The people came from far and – – – –,
The wonder-bird to see and – – – –.

3

Find as many words as you can that rhyme
with "**bean**".

1

pain   rain   remain   Spain

"Would you like to go to – – – – –,
Where there's hardly any – – – –?"
"No not I, here I'll – – – – – –,
Too much sun gives me a – – – –."

2

Gail   pain   strain   tail

A naughty girl whose name was – – – –,
Pulled a donkey by the – – – –,
The donkey kicked, she felt a – – – –,
When she sat down it was a – – – – – –.

3

Write down as many words as you can with the
same ending as "**train**".

1

away   day   play   today

Sorry, I can't come out to – – – –,
I have to stay indoors – – – – –,
But when my spots have gone – – – –,
I'll be out playing every – – –.

2

play   clay   way   pray
holiday   say   day   may

I made a model out of c – – –,
It came to life, began to p – – –,
I said, "Excuse me,—tell me p – – –,
Who gave you leave to play this w – –?"
He said, "Forgive me, but, I s – –,
Can't I have just one h – – – – – –?"
I said to him, "All right, you m – –."
We played together all the d – –.

3

How many words can you find that rhyme with "**hay**"?

16

1

food   good   moon   spoon

Worms are my favourite – – – –,
They are juicy and really – – – –,
I go on the lawn by the light of the – – – –,
And sup them up with a wooden – – – – –.

2

book   cook   cool   fool

A hungry rook once tried to – – – –,
A dish he read of in a – – – –,
He burned his beak, the silly – – – –,
He did not wait till it was – – – –.

3

Find as many words as you can that rhyme
with "**stood**".

1 been   deer   queen   queer

"Tell me have you ever – – – –,
To Fairyland to see the – – – – –?"
"Yes and it was rather – – – – –,
She rode upon a baby – – – –."

2 bee   glee   knee   tree

One day a busy little – – –,
Was buzzing happily, full of – – – –,
But then he bumped into a – – – –,
And needed plasters on every – – – –.

3 Make a list of the words you can think of with
the same ending as "**free**".

1

bound   found   hound   ground

A really big, enormous – – – – –,
Came at me with a single – – – – –,
He licked my face and soon I – – – – –,
That I was lying on the – – – – – –.

2

around   mound   pound   sound

As I was wandering – – – – – –,
I stopped to look at a grassy – – – – –,
And lying there, I found a – – – – –,
I picked it up without a – – – – –.

3

How many words can you find with the same
ending as "**around**"?

19

1

glue   **overdue**   **queue**   **Sue**

Once a girl whose name was – – –,
Was waiting in a big long – – – – –,
The bus was stuck, and – – – – – – –,
She asked if it was stuck with – – – –.

2

cruel   **due**   **flue**   **gruel**

The little chimney sweep was – – –,
To climb up the chimney and sweep the – – – –,
They fed him only tasteless – – – – –,
Don't you think that that was – – – – –?

3

How many words can you find with "**ue**" in them?

20

1

flew   knew   view   yew

In the churchyard, by the – – –,
An eerie figure came into – – – –,
It wasn't anyone I – – – –,
So, just in case, away I – – – –.

2

chew   new   Phew   stew

I hate it when I have to – – – –,
The lumps of meat in auntie's – – – –,
When they're all done, I just go, "– – – –!"
And hope the pudding's something – – –.

3   Find as many words as you can with the same
ending as "**blew**".

21

1

duck   luck   Puck   truck

A fairy once whose name was – – – –,
Went sailing on a tufted – – – –,
Went riding on an eight-wheeled – – – – –,
Some fairies do have all the – – – –.

2

boat   coat   pond   wet

He ran quite quickly to the – – – –,
To sail his little – – – –,
A shower came on, he got quite – – –,
He should have worn a – – – –.

3

How many words can you find that begin
with "**qu**"?

1

Fred   sped   truck   stuck

Billy on his little – – – – –,
Crashed on a hill and he was – – – – –,
Along came a helpful man called – – – –,
Who freed him and off Billy – – – –.

2

chance   dance   France   prance

Little Molly liked to – – – – –,
Round and round the room she'd – – – – – –,
I think that she would dance to – – – – – –,
If she ever got the – – – – – –.

3 Write down all the words you can find
that begin with "**wh**".

1

chin   shin   skin   twin

Melanie who was a – – – –,
Slipped on a banana – – – –,
Down she fell and cracked her – – – –,
And got a bruise right down her – – – –.

2

bank   guard   hard   prank

The boys decided that as a – – – – –,
They would take a toy gun into the – – – –,
But they had forgotten about the – – – – –,
He boxed their ears, it was very – – – –.

3

How many words can you find that rhyme with
"**tank**"?

1

fool   me   stool   tea

"Fetch my slippers, fetch my – – –,"
My big brother roared at – –.
"Fetch my paper, fetch my – – – – –."
"Fetch it yourself you silly – – – –."

2

cool   rank   school   tank

I'll be a soldier of high – – – –,
I'll make them drive me in a – – – –,
I'll man the gun, I'll be so – – – –,
My very first target will be the – – – – – –.

3

Find as many words as you can that end with
"**tch**", like "**fetch**".

1

cropping   **flopping**   **hopping**   **popping**

When Bobby Bunny started – – – – – – –,
His ears and bobtail started – – – – – – – –,
The long green grass he started – – – – – – – –,
Into his hole he'll soon be – – – – – – –.

2

knitting   **sitting**   **wrapping**   **yapping**

Dear old Granny was quietly – – – – – – –,
In her rocker quietly – – – – – – – –,
Along came the puppy, loudly – – – – – – –,
And granny's wool around him – – – – – – – –.

3

Write down all the words you can find to rhyme
with "**shopping**".

1

Kitty   Milly   pretty   silly

Did you hear of little – – – – –,
Who was really very – – – – –?
One day she hit her best friend – – – – –,
Because the boys said she was – – – – – –.

2

baby-sitter   glitter   litter   twitter

Ronnie spilled a tube of – – – – – – –,
On our silly – – – – –– – – – – –,
At that she began to – – – – – – –,
About our Ronnie dropping – – – – – –.

3

Find as many words as you can that rhyme
with "**silly**".

27

1

eye   fright   high   right

Little Bertie got a – – – – – –,
Mother said it served him – – – – –,
He fell down and cut his – – –,
Next time, he may not climb so – – – –.

2

fright   might   night   white

When I was walking out one – – – – –,
I saw a ghost, oh what a – – – – – –!
It was a huge thing dressed in – – – – –,
I ran away with all my – – – – –.

3

How many words can you find that rhyme with
"**frying**"?

1

flight   high   light   sky

Freda, the fairy, was so – – – – –,
When the wind blew she took – – – – – –,
Up and up into the – – –,
She got dizzy up so – – – –.

2

my   pie   sight   tonight

Grandpa said, "Oh my, oh – –,
I broke my false teeth on that – – –,
And I was going out – – – – – – –,
Without my teeth, I'll look a – – – – –."

3 See how many words you can find that rhyme
with "**fly**" and have the same ending.

1

by   light   night   try

Billy took a little – – – – –,
And ventured out into the – – – – –,
He said that he was going to – – –,
To catch a shooting star passing – –.

2

bright   eyes   tonight   ties

In her hair, a bow she – – – –,
She puts make-up on her – – – –,
She wears lipstick that is – – – – – –,
The boys will get a laugh – – – – – – –.

3

How many words can you find with the same
ending as "**flight**"?

1   **does   might   round   right**

The teacher says the world goes – – – – –,
I wonder if he's – – – – –.
It doesn't feel as if it – – – –,
But I suppose it – – – – –.

2   **edge   picture   pretty   sledge**

I sewed a woollen – – – – – – –,
Of Santa on his – – – – – –.
It turned out very – – – – – –,
With framing round the – – – –.

3   **all   feet   street   uniform**

The policeman said, "Good evening, – – –,"
When he came down the – – – – – –.
He wore a policeman's – – – – – – –,
And he had big flat – – – –.

1

because   **beside**   **house**   **mouse**

The chocolate soldier stood – – – – – –,
The chocolate soldier's – – – – –.
The chocolate soldier jumped – – – – – – –,
He saw a chocolate – – – – –.

2

doors   **goes**   **nose**   **snores**

When granny blows her noisy – – – –,
She scares the cat and off it – – – –,
But even worse is when she – – – – – –,
The windows rattle and the – – – – –.

3

crowd   **loud**   **goal**   **ground**

I like to be in the football – – – – – –,
When there's a great big – – – – –,
And when the striker scores a – – – –,
The cheering's very – – – –.

TLS 1